Antonio Vivaldi
THE FOUR SEASONS

Transcription for Piano solo

RICORDI

Please visit our websites:
www.ricordi.it - www.ricordi.com

Cover design by Giorgio Fioravanti

NR 138995
ISMN 979-0-041-38995-0

The Four Seasons ("Le quattro stagioni") from *"The Trial of Harmony and Invention"* ("Il cimento dell'armonia e dell'inventione"), op. VIII

In an enormously prolific age, Antonio Vivaldi (born March 4, 1678 in Venice – died 1741) was one of the most prolific and influential composers. His compositions and his services as a violin virtuoso were in demand all over Europe, but he chose to center his activities in Venice. For nearly forty years he was the Music Director of the *Pio Ospedale della Pietà*, one of the most famous Venetian conservatories for girls.

Even since their first publication in 1725, *The Four Seasons* have collectively been known as one of the most significant compositions of their author. The number of adaptation and imitations that they inspired in Vivaldi's own lifetime, to say nothing of later ages, is proof enough of that. The revival of *The Four Seasons* in the twentieth century was a little delayed. To Alceo Toni belongs the dual merit of having been the first person to draw public attention to the originality and artistic quality of *The Four Seasons* (1919) and the first to prepare a modern edition (a reduction for piano duet).

The autograph manuscripts of *The Four Seasons* have not survived (Vivaldi wrote out at least two autograph manuscripts). *The Four Seasons* were only the first of a set of twelve concertos which Vivaldi published in 1725 under the collective title of *"The Trial of Harmony and Invention"* ("Il cimento dell'armonia e dell'inventione"), Opus VIII. The first edition of Vivaldi's Opus VIII, in which *The Four Seasons* appears as Nos. 1-4, was published in Amsterdam in 1725 by Michel-Charles Le Cène. The title of the collection, *"The Trial of Harmony and Invention"*, remains enigmatic. It may be regarded as an allusion to the composer's compositional method as demonstrated in Op. VIII: the concept of a test for, and combination of, both the traditional craft of composition ("armonia") and the capricious imagination ("inventione").

As Op. VIII uniquely reveals, Vivaldi served the dedicatee, Václav Morzin (1676-1737), a distant cousin of Haydn's patrons, as "maestro di musica in Italia" (*"maestro* in Italy"*)*. In the dedication Vivaldi expresses the hope that the concertos may seem also new not only for the reason he is prefacing each concerto with an explanatory sonnet, but also because much of the musical depiction itself has been expanded. The degree of programmatic elaboration encountered in *The Four Seasons* – in the individual concertos and still more in the cycle taken as a whole – exceeds that found in similar concertos so massively that it is hard not to believe that a full-scale "scenario", albeit originally private and covert, existed from the start. The sonnets themselves were not, in any simple sense, this scenario; they were "on" ("sopra") the concertos rather than the other way round.

Vivaldi's autorship of the sonnets can be readily accepted. They are neither better nor worse as poetry than the many specimens of his literary craft identified in the text of his cantatas and operatic arias. Their language, lightly contaminated by venetianism (e.g., "mossoni", "giaccio"), is consistent with the prose of his letters. To avoid any possible misunderstanding of his "program" music, Vivaldi has each line of the sonnets printed again over the precise passage of the music it explains; and he even prints further clarifying words.

IV

Sonetto dimostrativo
sopra il concerto intitolato
La primavera
del Sig.ʳᵉ D. Antonio Vivaldi

A Giunt'è la primavera, e festosetti
B la salutan gl'augei con lieto canto,
C e i fonti allo spirar de' Zeffiretti
   con dolce mormorio scorrono intanto.

D Vengon coprendo l'aer di nero ammanto
   e lampi e tuoni ad annunziarla eletti:
E indi tacendo questi gl'augelletti
   tornan di nuovo al lor canoro incanto:

F e quindi sul fiorito ameno prato
   al caro mormorio di fronde e piante
   dorme 'l caprar col fido can a lato.

G Di pastoral zampogna al suon festante
   danzan ninfe e pastor nel tetto amato
   di primavera all'apparir brillante.

Explanatory Sonnet
on the Concerto Entitled
Spring
by Don Antonio Vivaldi

Spring has arrived, and joyfully
the birds greet her with glad song,
while at Zephyr's breath the streams
flow forth with a sweet murmur.

Her chosen heralds, thunder and lightning,
come to envelop the air in a black cloak;
once they have fallen silent, the little birds
return anew to their melodious incantation:

then on the pleasant, flower-bedecked meadow,
to the happy murmur of fronds and plants,
the goatherd sleeps next to his trusty dog.

To the festive sound of rustic bagpipes
nymphs and shepherds dance beneath the beloved sky
at the glorious appearance of spring.

Sonetto dimostrativo
sopra il concerto intitolato
L'estate
del Sig.ʳᵉ D. Antonio Vivaldi

A Sotto dura stagion dal sole accesa
   langue l'uom, langue 'l gregge ed arde il pino;
B scioglie il cucco la voce, e tosto intesa
C canta la tortorella e 'l gardellino.

D Zeffiro dolce spira, ma contesa
   muove Borea improvviso al suo vicino;
E e piange il pastorel perché sospesa
   teme fiera borasca e 'l suo destino.

F Toglie alle membra lasse il suo riposo
   il timore de' lampi e tuoni fieri
   e de' mosche e mossoni il stuol furioso.

G Ah che pur troppo i suoi timor son veri:
   tuona e fulmina il ciel, e grandinoso
   tronca il capo alle spiche e a' grani alteri.

Explanatory Sonnet
on the Concerto Entitled
Summer
by Don Antonio Vivaldi

In a harsh season burned by the sun,
man and flock languish, and the pine tree is scorched;
the cuckoo unleashes its voice, and soon
we hear the songs of the turtle-dove and the goldfinch.

Sweet Zephyr blows, but Boreas suddenly
opens a dispute with his neighbour;
and the shepherd laments his fate
for he fears a fierce squall is coming.

His weary limbs are robbed of rest
by his fear of fierce thunder and lightning
and by the furious swarm of flies and blowflies.

Alas, his fears are only too real:
the sky fills with thunder and lightning,
and hailstones hew off the heads of proud cornstalks.

Sonetto dimostrativo
sopra il concerto intitolato
L'autunno
del Sig.^{re} D. Antonio Vivaldi

A Celebra il villanel con balli e canti
    del felice raccolto il bel piacere,
B e del liquor di Bacco accesi, tanti
C finiscono col sonno il lor godere.

D Fa ch'ogn'uno tralasci e balli e canti
    l'aria, che temperata dà piacere,
    e la stagion, ch'invita tanti e tanti
    d'un dolcissimo sonno al bel godere.

E I cacciator alla nov'alba a caccia
    con corni, schioppi e cani escono fuore;
F fugge la belva e seguono la traccia;

G già sbigottita e lassa al gran rumore
    de' schioppi e cani, ferita minaccia
H languida di fuggir, ma oppressa muore.

Explanatory Sonnet
on the Concerto Entitled
Autumn
by Don Antonio Vivaldi

The countryman celebrates with dance and song
the sweet pleasure of a good harvest,
and many, fired by the liquor of Bacchus,
end their enjoyment by falling asleep.

Everyone is made to abandon singing and dancing
by the temperate air, which gives pleasure,
and by the season, which invites so many
to enjoy the sweetness of sleep.

The huntsmen come out at the crack of dawn
with their horns, guns and hounds;
the quarry flees and they track it:

already terrified and tired out by the great noise
of the guns and hounds, the wounded beast
makes a feeble effort to flee but dies in agony.

Sonetto dimostrativo
sopra il concerto intitolato
L'inverno
del Sig.^{re} D. Antonio Vivaldi

A Aggiacciato tremar tra nevi algenti
B al severo spirar d'orrido vento;
C correr battendo i piedi ogni momento;
D e pel soverchio gel batter i denti;

E passar al foco i dì quieti e contenti
    mentre la pioggia fuor bagna ben cento;
F camminar sopra 'l giaccio e a passo lento
G per timor di cader girsene intenti;

H gir forte, sdrucciolar, cader a terra;
I di nuovo ir sopra 'l giaccio e correr forte
L sin ch'il giaccio si rompe e si disserra;

M sentir uscir dalle ferrate porte
N Sirocco, Borea e tutti i venti in guerra:
    quest'è 'l verno, ma tal che gioia apporte.

Explanatory Sonnet
on the Concerto Entitled
Winter
by Don Antonio Vivaldi

To shiver, frozen, amid icy snow
in the bitter blast of a horrible wind;
to run, constantly stamping one's feet;
and to feel one's teeth chatter on account of the excessive cold;

to spend restful, happy days at the fireside
while the rain outside drenches a good hundred;
to walk on the ice, and with slow steps
to move about cautiously for fear of falling;

to go fast, to slip and fall down;
to go on the ice again and run fast
until the ice cracks and opens up;

to hear coming out of the iron gates
Sirocco, Boreas and all the winds at war:
that's winter, but of a kind to gladden one's heart.

Antonio Vivaldi *(1678-1741)*

CONCERTO in E MAJOR
originally for solo violin, strings and continuo

"SPRING„ ("La primavera") Op. VIII n. 1 - F. I n. 22

Transcription for piano

Spring has arrived,

BIRDS IN SONG

and joyfully

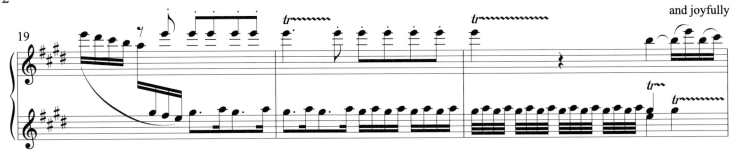

the birds greet her with glad song,

FLOWING STREAMS
while at Zephyr's breath the streams

legato

flow forth with a sweet murmur.

THUNDERS
Her chosen heralds, thunder and

lightning, come to envelop the air in a black cloak;

BIRDS IN SONG
once they have fallen silent, the little birds return anew to their melodious

incantation:

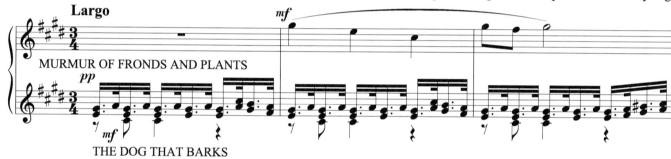

THE SLUMBERING GOATHERD

then on the pleasant, flower-bedecked meadow, to the happy murmur of fronds and plants, the goatherd sleeps next to his trusty dog.

Largo

MURMUR OF FRONDS AND PLANTS

THE DOG THAT BARKS

6

138995

RUSTIC DANCE

To the festive sound of rustic bagpipes nymphs and shepherds dance beneath the beloved sky at the glorious appearance of spring.

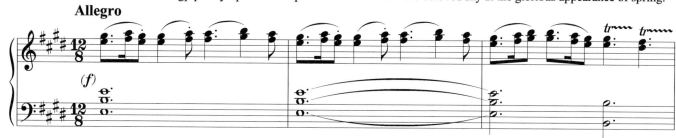

Antonio Vivaldi (1678-1741)

CONCERTO in G MINOR

originally for solo violin, strings and continuo

"SUMMER„ ("L'estate") Op. VIII n. 2 - F. I n. 23

Transcription for piano

LANGUOR FOR THE HEAT
In a harsh season burned by the sun, man and flock languish, and the pine tree is scorched;

Allegro non molto

THE CUCKOO
the cuckoo unleashes its voice,

Allegro *e tutto sopra il canto*

(Allegro non molto)

THE TURTLE-
and soon we

DOVE
hear the songs of the turtle-dove and the goldfinch.

THE GOLDFINCH

SWEET ZEPHYRS
Sweet Zephyr blows,

14

pp   p   pp   f

with his neighbour;

BOREAS WIND

(mp)

and the shepherd laments his fate for he fears a fierce squall is

coming.

His weary limbs are robbed of rest by his fear of fierce thunder and lightning and by the furious swarm of flies and blowflies.

18 BLUSTERING SUMMER WEATHER
Alas, his fears are only too real: the sky fills with thunder and lightning, and hailstones hew off the heads of proud cornstalks.

Antonio Vivaldi *(1678-1741)*

CONCERTO in F MAJOR

originally for solo violin, strings and continuo

"AUTUMN„ ("L'autunno") Op. VIII n. 3 - F. I n. 24

Transcription for piano

DANCING AND SINGING COUNTRYMEN
The countryman celebrates with dance and song the sweet pleasure of a good harvest,

* Edition Le Cène:

138995

24

THE DRUNKARD
and many, fired by the liquor of

Bacchus,

DRUNKARDS

DRUNKARDS

* Sic.

end their enjoyment by falling asleep.

DOZING DRUNKARDS

Everyone is made to abandon singing and dancing by the temperate air, which gives pleasure, and by the season, which invites so

Adagio molto

many to enjoy the sweetness of sleep.

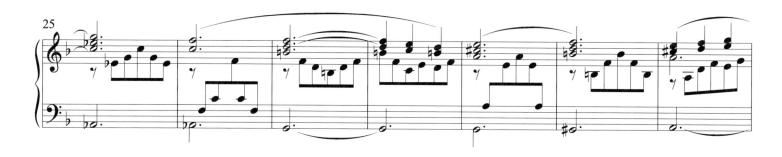

THE HUNT

The huntsmen come out at the crack of dawn with their horns, guns and hounds;

Allegro

THE FLEEING BEAST OF PREY
the quarry flees and they track it;

GUNSHOTS AND DOGS
already terrified and tired out by the great noise

of the guns and hounds, the wounded beast

THE FLEEING PREY DIES
makes a feeble effort to flee but dies in agony.

Antonio Vivaldi (1678-1741)

CONCERTO in F MINOR

originally for solo violin, strings and continuo

"WINTER„ ("L'inverno") Op. VIII n. 4 - F. I n. 25

Transcription for piano

To shiver, frozen, amid icy snow

Allegro molto

HORRIBLE WIND
in the bitter blast of a horrible wind;

RUNNING ABOUT AND STAMPING ONE'S FEET FOR THE COLD
to run, constantly stamping one's feet;

and to feel one's teeth chatter on account of the excessive cold;

to spend restful, happy days at the fireside while the rain outside drenches a good hundred;

to walk on the ice,

WALKING SLOWLY AND CAUTIOUSLY
and with slow steps to move about cau-

tiously for fear of falling;

to go fast, to slip and fall down;

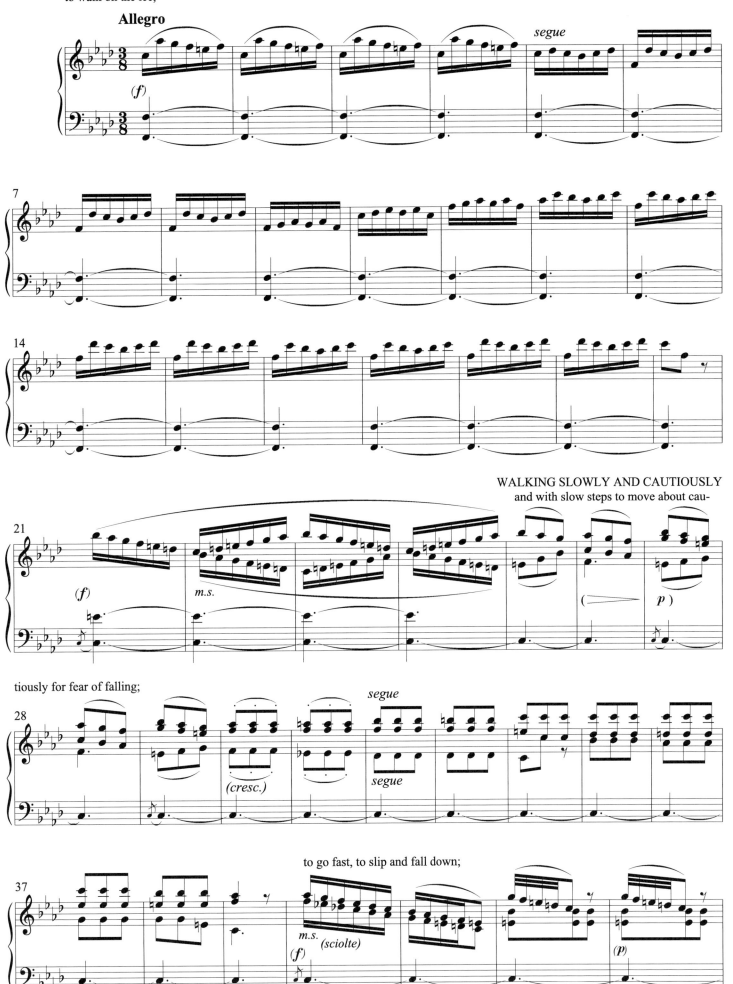

44

FALLING TO THE GROUND

RUNNING FAST
to go on the ice again and run fast

51

58

65

72

78

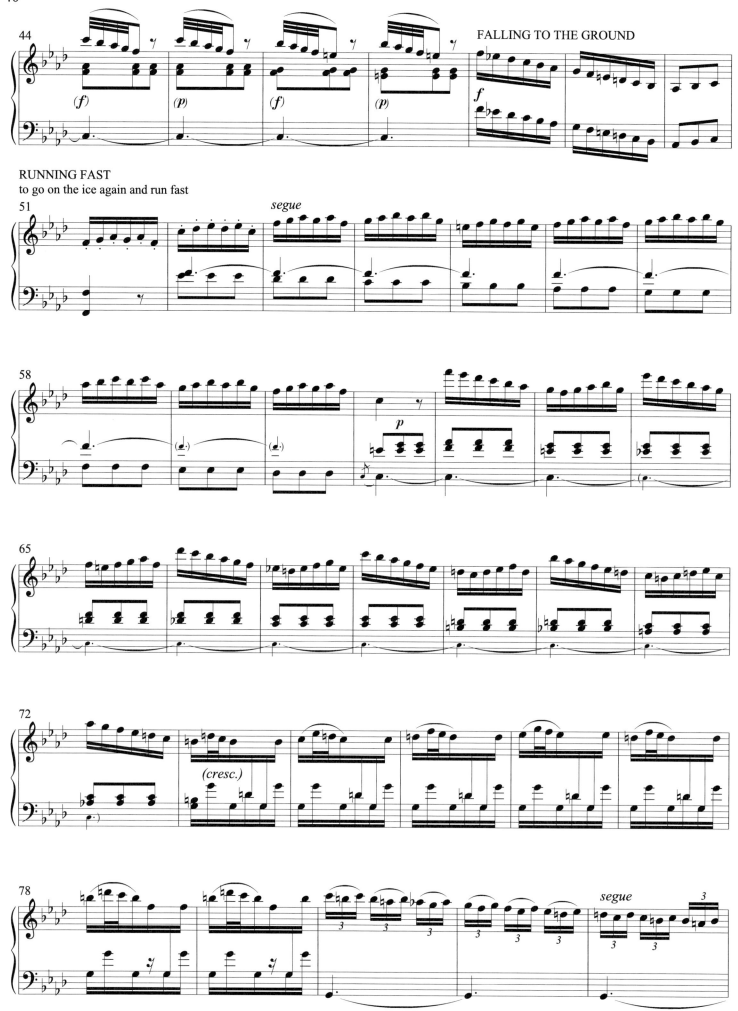

until the ice cracks and opens up;

THE SIROCCO WIND
to hear coming out of the iron gates

THE BOREAS WIND AND ALL THE WINDS
Sirocco, Boreas and all the winds at war:

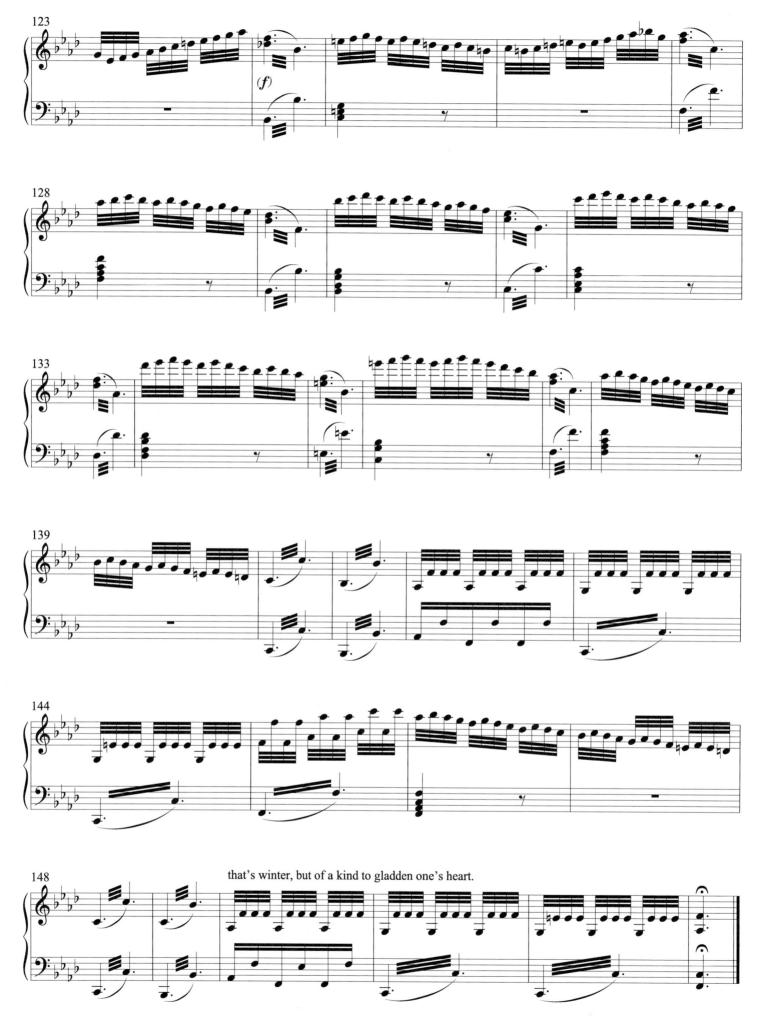

that's winter, but of a kind to gladden one's heart.